Spider-Man Presents the
MARVEL
JOKE BOOK

Autumn
Publishing

Published in 2019
by Autumn Publishing
Cottage Farm
Sywell
NN6 0BJ
www.igloobooks.com

Autumn is an imprint of Bonnier Books UK

© 2019 MARVEL

GOL002 0419
2 4 6 8 10 9 7 5 3 1
ISBN 978-1-78905-847-5

Printed and manufactured in China

I'M HERE TO TURN **YOU** INTO A WORLD-CLASS COMEDIAN. WE'LL START WITH THE BASICS AND THEN... LET'S JUST SAY, BY THE TIME THIS IS ALL OVER YOU'LL BE A LEAN, MEAN JOKE MACHINE. **BUCKLE UP, BUTTERCUP!** GET READY TO LEARN FROM THE BEST – ME!

Oh, like we're supposed to follow you because you're a comedy genius or something?

YES. **NOW BEAT IT, ANT-BOY!**

The name is Ant-Man. **ANT-MAN.**

GO AWAY. IT'S NOT YOUR TIME YET!

HOW TO TELL A JOKE

COMEDY COMES IN MANY DIFFERENT FORMS.
THE MOST COMMON FORM IS
THE JOKE!

HERE ARE SOME TIPS ON HOW
TO TELL A GOOD JOKE.

Step #1: Choose a joke

FIND A JOKE THAT **YOU** THINK IS FUNNY. THAT WAY
YOU'LL LOVE TELLING IT TO PEOPLE.

Step #2: Figure it out

JOKES HAVE TWO THINGS: A SET-UP AND A PUNCH LINE.

Example:

Q: What happens when a banana
gets sunburnt?

THIS IS THE **SET-UP.** IT PRESENTS THE IDEA OF THE JOKE
AND GETS YOUR AUDIENCE THINKING ABOUT WHAT
THE ANSWER MIGHT BE.

A: It peels!

THIS IS THE **PUNCH LINE.** IT'S WHERE YOU GET THE
LAUGHS! IT'S SURPRISING AND FUN. IT CAN ALSO
MAKE PEOPLE THINK.

Step #3: Prepare

REHEARSE YOUR JOKE! YOU WANT TO MAKE SURE YOU TELL IT
AWESOMELY.

Step #4: Perform

CHOOSE AN AUDIENCE, LIKE A FRIEND OR FAMILY MEMBER.
DON'T TELL THEM YOU'RE ABOUT TO LAY DOWN SOME
HYSTERICAL HUMOUR. NO NEED TO BE NERVOUS, EITHER –
YOU'VE GOT THIS! SPEAK CLEARLY AND, MOST IMPORTANTLY,
HAVE FUN.

HILARIOUS COMEDY LEGENDS LIKE **ME** AREN'T BORN OVERNIGHT.

WE'LL BE COVERING LOTS OF DIFFERENT TYPES OF JOKES. CHECK OUT A FEW EXAMPLES:

KNOCK-KNOCK

Knock, knock.
Who's there?
Radio.
Radio who?
Radio not, here we go!

Questions & Answers

Q: Why did Peter Parker eat his maths homework?

A: Because his teacher said it was a piece of cake.

TONGUE TWISTERS

ELECTRO LICKED THE LIZARD'S LABEL.
ELECTRO LICKED THE LIZARD'S LABEL.
ELECTRO LICKED THE LIZARD'S LABEL.

SOUNDS **WEIRD** TO ME.

NOW THAT YOU'VE LEARNT THE BASICS, LET'S DO SOME CLASSIC **KNOCK-KNOCK JOKES**. GIVE 'EM A TRY.

Knock, knock.
Who's there?
Nun.
Nun who?
Nun of your business.

Knock, knock.
Who's there?
Meyer.
Meyer who?
Meyer nosy.

Knock, knock.
Who's there?
Pecan.
Pecan who?
Pecan somebody your own size!

Knock, knock.
Who's there?
Zany.
Zany who?
Zany body in there?

KNOCK-
KNOCK

Knock, knock.
Who's there?
Fairy.
Fairy who?
**Fairy nice to meet you,
I'm Spider-Man!**

Knock, knock.
Who's there?
Lena.
Lena who?
**Lena little bit closer
and I'll tell you.**

Knock, knock.
Who's there?
Dare.
Dare who?
**Dare must be some
mistake, you're in
my house!**

Knock, knock.
Who's there?
Penny.
Penny who?
**Penny for your
thoughts?**

MY THOUGHTS ARE
WORTH WAAAY MORE
THAN A PENNY. THEY'RE
WORTH A DOLLAR
AT LEAST.

KNOCK-
KNOCK

Knock, knock.
Who's there?
Noah.
Noah who?
Noah good place to get a slice of pizza around here? I'm starving.

Knock, knock.
Who's there?
Stan.
Stan who?
Stan back! I'm knocking this door down!

Knock, knock.
Who's there?
Rita.
Rita who?
Rita book sometime. You might learn something.

Knock, knock.
Who's there?
Dots.
Dots who?
Dots for me to know and you to find out.

Knock, knock.
Who's there?
Juicy.
Juicy who?
Juicy what I just saw?

Knock, knock.
Who's there?
Jamaica.
Jamaica who?
Jamaica great lasagna!

Knock, knock.
Who's there?
Wooden shoe.
Wooden shoe who?
**Wooden shoe like
to know?**

Knock, knock.
Who's there?
Weird.
Weird who?
**Weird you hide the
chocolate?!**

I'M GETTING
SUPER HUNGRY
NOW.

KNOCK-
KNOCK

13

TIME FOR SOME
**QUESTIONS &
ANSWERS!**

Q: What do you call a rude cow with a twitch?
A: Beef jerky.

Q: Why are spiders like toy tops?
A: They are always spinning!

Q: What is a Super Hero's favourite
part of the joke?
A: The punch line!

Q: What has two legs but can't walk?
A: A pair of trousers.

Questions
& Answers

Q: What breaks when Spider-Man
starts talking?
A: The silence.

Q: What is a Super Hero's favourite drink?
A: Fruit punch!

Q: What do you call a pig with three eyes?
A: A piiig.

Q: What do you call a snowman's parents?
A: Mum and Popsicle.

Questions
& Answers

Q: What does a Super Hero
put in their drink?
A: Just ice.

Q: Why did the baby cookie cry?
A: Because its mum was a wafer so long.

Q: What kind of songs are
balloons afraid of?
A: Pop songs.

Q: Why did the teacher wear glasses?
A: Because her class was so bright.

HOW'S IT GOING?
FEELING GOOD?
FEELING LIKE A
COMEDIAN
YET?

Questions
& Answers

17

Q: What is Spider-Man's favourite
kind of rice?
A: Sticky rice!

Q: Why did the potato cross the road?
A: It saw a fork up ahead.

Q: What did Iron Man get for
acting up in class?
A: De-TIN-tion!

Q: What type of key opens a banana?
A: A mon-key.

Questions
& Answers

ME: I'M THE HARDEST WORKER. MY BOSS LOVES ME. I DESERVE A PAY RISE!

ALSO ME, AT WORK:

Q: What's Peter Parker's night-time job?
A: He's a web designer.

Q: What does Spider-Man eat
with a cheeseburger?
A: French flies!

Q: What do you call
an undercover spider?
A: A spy-duuuurr!

Q: What do you call Spider-Man and his new
wife right after they get married?
A: Newly webs.

**WHAT'S THE
DIFFERENCE BETWEEN
LOVE AND MARRIAGE?
LOVE IS BLIND
AND MARRIAGE IS A REAL
EYE-OPENER.**

Questions
& Answers

Q: Where does Spider-Man go
to find information?

A: The World Wide Web.

Q: Why is Spider-Man a good
baseball player?

A: He knows how to catch flies!

**GET IT?
FLY BALLS? CATCH FLIES?
YOU GOT IT...**

Q: Why did Spider-Man rent a car?

A: So he could take it out for a spin.

Q: Did you hear about
Spider-Man's love life?

A: It's a very tangled web.

Q: What do you call the Irish Spider-Man?
A: Paddy Longlegs!

**THERE'S AN
IRISH SPIDER-MAN?!**
SOMEBODY CALL MY LAWYER.

Q: What's Spider-Man's favourite dance?
A: The jitterbug.

Q: Why did Spider-Man join the swimming team?
A: Because he had webbed feet.

Questions
& Answers

COSTUME PATROL

THWIP OR THWOP?

> HOLD UP JUST ONE MINUTE. I DID NOT OKAY THIS SECTION. **STOP THIS.** STOP THIS, I SAY! THIS IS MY SHOW!

BLACK PANTHER:
What a crybaby. His colour scheme and web pattern are unnatural. I've never met a spider that looked and acted like this.

BLACK WIDOW:
From one spider to another, this suit is a little too on the nose. Wait, do spiders have noses?

DOCTOR STRANGE:
Spiders are naturally hairy. I would have liked to have seen a lot more hair. And fangs! Why don't I just turn him into a REAL spider?

I LOVE ME SOME **TONGUE TWISTERS!** TRY SAYING THESE THREE TIMES REALLY FAST.

A BIG BLACK BUG BIT A BIG BLACK BEAR.
A BIG BLACK BUG BIT A BIG BLACK BEAR.
A BIG BLACK BUG BIT A BIG BLACK BEAR.

RED LEATHER, YELLOW LEATHER.
RED LEATHER, YELLOW LEATHER.
RED LEATHER, YELLOW LEATHER.

PRETTY PINK PIGGY BANK.
PRETTY PINK PIGGY BANK.
PRETTY PINK PIGGY BANK.

SILLY SALLY SELLS SCENTED SHINGLES.
SILLY SALLY SELLS SCENTED SHINGLES.
SILLY SALLY SELLS SCENTED SHINGLES.

BARRY BAGLEY BROUGHT A BUTTERED BISCUIT.
BARRY BAGLEY BROUGHT A BUTTERED BISCUIT.
BARRY BAGLEY BROUGHT A BUTTERED BISCUIT.

 PETER PARKER PICKED A PECK OF PICKLED PEPPERS.
HOW MANY PICKLED PEPPERS DID PETER PARKER PICK?
PETER PARKER PICKED A PECK OF PICKLED PEPPERS.
HOW MANY PICKLED PEPPERS DID PETER PARKER PICK?
PETER PARKER PICKED A PECK OF PICKLED PEPPERS.
HOW MANY PICKLED PEPPERS DID PETER PARKER PICK?

 CRAZY CRISP CRUSTS CRACKLE AND CRUNCH.
CRAZY CRISP CRUSTS CRACKLE AND CRUNCH.
CRAZY CRISP CRUSTS CRACKLE AND CRUNCH.

THIS IS MAKING ME HUNGRY!

TONGUE TWISTERS

THE SKIMPY SKUNK SAT ON A STUMP AND THUNK THE
STUMP STUNK, BUT THE STUMP THUNK THE SKUNK STUNK.
THE SKIMPY SKUNK SAT ON A STUMP AND THUNK THE
STUMP STUNK, BUT THE STUMP THUNK THE SKUNK STUNK.
THE SKIMPY SKUNK SAT ON A STUMP AND THUNK THE
STUMP STUNK, BUT THE STUMP THUNK THE SKUNK STUNK.

 TANGY TACOS TAUNT TERRY'S TASTE BUDS.
TANGY TACOS TAUNT TERRY'S TASTE BUDS.
TANGY TACOS TAUNT TERRY'S TASTE BUDS.

 I THOUGHT A THOUGHT. BUT THE
THOUGHT I THOUGHT WASN'T THE
THOUGHT I THOUGHT I THOUGHT.

PETER PARKER ALWAYS SEEMS TO DISAPPEAR WHEN SPIDER-MAN SHOWS UP.

BUT... THAT'S NONE OF MY BUSINESS.

ALLOW ME TO INTRODUCE YOU TO THE **AVENGERS** OF COMEDY!

WE'VE GOT **CAPTAIN AMERICA:** SUPER-YOUNG-LOOKING GRANDPA!

HULK: THE BIGGEST, GREENEST BABY YOU EVER DID SEE!

HAWKEYE: ALL ARROWS, ALL THE TIME!

THOR: PRETTY HAIR, MAN!

BLACK WIDOW: A VERY NICE LADY WHO'S GOOD AT FIGHTING! PLEASE DON'T HURT ME.

Thank you.

BLACK PANTHER: KING OF... SOMEPLACE FAR AWAY?

I AM THE KING OF WAKANDA.

I LIKE THAT TITLE BETTER. **TAKE IT AWAY, 'VENGIES!** (THAT'S A CUTE LITTLE NICKNAME I JUST MADE UP.)

Q: What's Thor's favourite food?
A: Thor-tillas.

*'Tis true! I, son of Odin, do **enjoy** a yummy snack.*

Q: What do you call Iron Man without his suit?
A: Stark naked!

Q: When do ducks wake up?
A: The quack of dawn.

HA, HA, HA! QUACK OF DAWN! HULK LIKE JOKE!

Q: Why should you eat a cupcake in the rain?
A: You'll get more sprinkles!

Questions & Answers

Q: What did Iron Man win for coming in first place?
A: A gold metal!

True. Remember, I'm good at EVERYTHING.

Q: Why did the orange stop in the middle of the road?
A: It ran out of juice!

Q: What did Thor become after he wrote a book?
A: An author.

Q: What do you give Hulk when he's feeling ill?
A: Plenty of room!

Hulk no like that joke.

Q: What's Black Panther's favourite
day of the week?
A: Cat-urday.

I'M NOT AN **ACTUAL** CAT.
YOU KNOW THAT, RIGHT?

Q: Why is Iron Man like a
Russian nesting doll?
A: Because he's full of himself.

HEY! That's not totally true! (But I do
look amazing underneath all this armour.)

Q: What do you call a guy that
looks like Thor's brother?
A: A Loki-like.

Questions
& Answers

Q: What did the police do when the
evil barber escaped from prison?
A: They combed the area.

BECAUSE HE'S A BARBER! HA!

Q: What's Hulk's favourite side dish?
A: Smashed potatoes.

Q: What did the archer wear
to a formal event?
A: A bow tie!

Captain America ● @CapRules1920
Hello? Is anyone there? I would like to make a post. This is Captain America. I am an Avenger. U can look it up ok. My secret identity is St

Captain America ● @CapRules1920
Cap again. Got cut off. I'm very new to this technology. I was trapped in a block of ice at the bottom of the ocean. Give me a break.

Captain America ● @CapRules1920
How is everyone doing? WOW what a great place to record my thoughts. AND tell you my FAV dance moves. POP AND LOCK BABY!!!

Captain America ● @CapRules1920
That last one was a joke. HA. Is anyone there? I would like to place an order for a large cheese pizza. EXTRA ANCHOVIES for Hulk. Pls hurry!

COSTUME PATROL

DAGGER? DRAG HER!

Hey! Whoa. What is this? What's the Costume Patrol?

GAMORA: We are the costume patrol. You are in violation of our code. Garments of this colour will NOT be worn after Labour Day.

DOCTOR STRANGE: Meh. Not a fan of the bodysuit. Personally, I prefer a big, flowing cape. And where are the fun accessories? She needs more jewellery. LOTS of jewellery.

BLACK WIDOW: Watch it, Strange. Bodysuits allow a fighter to move effortlessly when dealing with an attacking opponent. Plus, they're SO easy to clean.

EASY TO CLEAN? HA! ONE SPILL OF MY FRUIT PUNCH AND IT'S OVER. MMMM. NOW I'M THIRSTY. FOR FASHION. OKURRRR!

Knock, knock.
Who's there?
Thor.
Thor who?
**Thor-y about some
of these jokes.**

Knock, knock.
Who's there?
Atch.
Atch who?
Bless you!

Hulk want to play!

GO FOR IT, BIG GUY.

Knock, knock.

WHO'S THERE?

Hulk.

HULK WHO?

Hulk **smash!**

**UH... THAT ONE DOESN'T MAKE ANY SENSE.
(PLEASE DON'T SMASH ME.)**

KNOCK-
KNOCK

Spidey's
OPEN MIC SPOTLIGHT:

COMING TO THE STAGE RIGHT NOW IS ONE OF THE **FIERCEST FIGHTERS** AROUND AND AN AMAZING AVENGER TO BOOT. LADIES AND GENTLEMAN, PUT YOUR HANDS TOGETHER FOR **BLACK WIDOW!**

Knock, knock.
Who's there?
A broken pencil.
A broken pencil who?
Never mind.
It's pointless.

Q: What do you get when you mix a toad with the sun?
A: Star warts.

Black Widow

Knock, knock.
Who's there?
Ooze.
Ooze who?
Ooze afraid of the big bad wolf?

Q: What's Squirrel Girl's
favourite ballet?
A: The Nutcracker.

Q: What do you call an elephant
that wears perfume?
A: A smell-e-phant.

Knock, knock.
Who's there?
Spell.
Spell who?
W-H-O.

Q: What do you call a
fake noodle?
A: An impasta.

Sometimes black widow spiders can
kill their mates.

UM, THAT'S **NOT** A JOKE. THAT'S JUST A FACT.

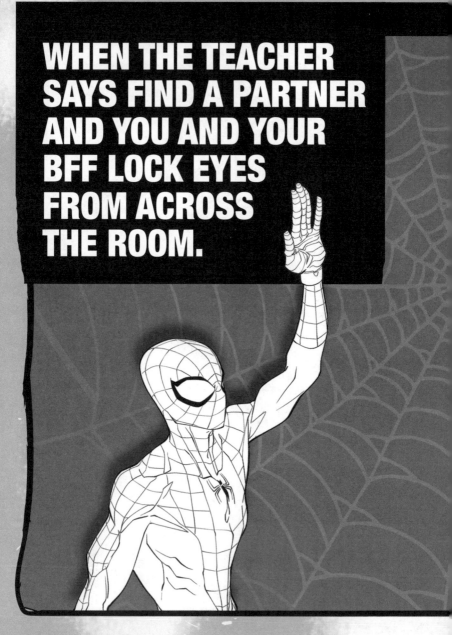

WHEN THE TEACHER SAYS FIND A PARTNER AND YOU AND YOUR BFF LOCK EYES FROM ACROSS THE ROOM.

Captain America ● @CapRules1920
No one lets me showcase my comedic skills. It's not fair! Oh well. I guess you could say I'm all Stars & GRIPES. Get it??? #LetCapBeCap

Captain America ● @CapRules1920
Just found out that Hulk is really good at gardening. Guess you could say he has a GREEN THUMB. U can share that one w/ friends if u want.

Captain America ● @CapRules1920
OK GOTTA GO. ULTRON ATTACKING. UGH THAT ROBOT REALLY KNOWS HOW TO PRESS MY BUTTONS. WAIT, MESSED THAT ONE UP. UGH VERY STRESSED! BRB

Captain America ● @CapRules1920
Logging off. Got to go to Asgard for a thing. One more joke! Why does Captain America never knock on doors? Because freedom rings. #CAPOUT

AND NOW...
BLACK PANTHER TELLS A JOKE!

YOU KNOW, I USED TO THINK I WAS A DOG.

REALLY?

YES. I WAS QUITE... **PURR**-PLEXED.

THIS HAS BEEN...
BLACK PANTHER TELLS A JOKE!

CAPTAIN AMERICA IS SO **OLD**.

 How **old** is he?

CAPTAIN AMERICA IS SO OLD, **HIS FIRST PET WAS A T. REX.**

 THAT'S **NOT** TRUE!

WHICH PART? THE PART ABOUT YOU BEING **OLD** OR THE PART ABOUT...

 MY FIRST PET WAS A GOLDFISH AND HIS NAME WAS FLUFFY!

THAT'S EVEN MORE EMBARRASSING...

THAT MOMENT WHEN A LITTLE GIRL ASKS YOU TO SIGN HER PICTURE OF SHREK.

49

HEY!
I'm not a loser!
I'm very well respected.
I'll have you know.
AND I can tell a
joke just fine.

WELL, C'MON
THEN, LET'S
HEAR ONE.

Knock, knock.

WHO'S THERE?

Duck!

DUCK WHO?

No, seriously, **DUCK!**
People are throwing things at us!

I GUESS I'LL LET THESE **WEIRDOS** HAVE A CHANCE.

Q: What's Doctor Octopus's favourite month?
A: October.

Q: Did you hear about the zombie hairdresser?
A: She dyed on the job.

Q: Where does Morbius the Living Vampire store his money?
A: In a blood bank.

Q: Where does a bee sit?
A: On its bee-hind.

Questions & Answers

Q: Why is the Lizard so good
at creeping up on people?
A: Because he's a crept-tile.

Q: What kinds of fish don't swim?
A: Dead ones.

THAT'S **HARSH.**

**We're villains. What
did you expect?**

Q: What do you call the Rhino
in a phone booth?
A: Stuck!

Q: How did the Vulture learn to fly?
A: He winged it.

Q: What crime did Doctor Octopus
commit at the bank?
A: Armed robbery.

Q: Why is Norman Osborn
such a messy eater?
A: Because he's always Goblin.

CLEVER!

Questions
& Answers

COSTUME PATROL

GUILTY AS CHARGED!

I WILL NOT BE JUDGED BY THE LIKES OF YOU!

CAPTAIN AMERICA: Thanos's outfit is a true crime of fashion. He should be jailed for his poor layering skills.

DOCTOR STRANGE: The chunky metal helmet isn't doing him any favours. What's he hiding under there? And why is he so angry?

HAWKEYE: He needs an accessory. Like a glove with a bunch of bright, colourful stones on it. Something that says, 'I'm in control of this universe, and I like it'.

DO NOT GIVE HIM ANY GLOVES. TRUST ME ON THIS.

Q: What was the Tyrannosaurus
rex's diagnosis?
A: He had a dino-sore throat.

Q: Why did the boy bring a skunk to school?
A: For show-and-smell.

Q: How do you make a spider float?
**A: Throw it in a root beer and add
two scoops of vanilla ice cream.**

Q: What kind of trousers
do ghosts wear?
A: Boo jeans.

Q: Why couldn't the snake talk?
A: He had a frog in his throat.

Q: What do pigs eat when
it's freezing outside?
A: Slop sickles.

Q: How did Doctor Octopus
prepare to battle Spider-Man?
A: He made sure he was well armed.

Maybe if I get MORE arms, I'll finally
be able to defeat Spider-Man!

Questions
& Answers

Q: When is a bogey not a bogey?
A: When it's snot.

Q: What kind of dog does Dracula own?
A: A bloodhound.

Q: Where is the best place to talk
to a giant slimy monster?
A: From far away!

Q: What's a sea monster's
favourite sandwich?
A: A sub!

Q: What did the zombie order
at the restaurant?
A: The waiter.

Q: What do sea monsters eat?
A: Fish and ships.

Q: What do you call a lizard
who likes hip-hop?
A: A rap-tile!

 Sssseriously ssssick, sssson.

 Questions
& Answers

Um. Hi.

IRON MAN: UGH. Where do I begin? This is what happens when you let lions and tigers give you advice on your outfit.

BLACK PANTHER: Men who stalk beasts for their hides are WEAK. I will show this one who is the hunter and who is the prey.

DOCTOR STRANGE: His mane looks so fluffy and fun! I wish I had a fluffy mane on my costume. Call me DOCTOR FLUFF.

I'D STICK WITH DOCTOR STRANGE. IT'S A BETTER CHOICE. BUT DON'T WORRY, YOU'LL ALWAYS BE MY MANE MAN. **BOOYAH!** SPIDEY DELIVERS THE KILLER JOKE!

IT'S TIME FOR SOME
YO MAMA JOKES!
JUST REMEMBER: THESE ARE JOKES.
THEY'RE MEANT TO BE DELIVERED IN THE
SPIRIT OF FUN! DON'T USE THEM TO
HURT PEOPLE. YO MAMA
WOULDN'T LIKE THAT.

YO MAMA loves
ice cream so much,
her blood type is chocolate chip!

YO MAMA's so old,
she took her driving test
on a dinosaur!

Yo Mama Jokes

YO MAMA is so short,
she uses a sock for
a sleeping bag!

YO MAMA's breath is so bad,
when she yawns, her teeth duck!

YO MAMA is so chatty,
the only place she's ever
invited is outside!

Yo Mama Jokes

YO MAMA is so mean that Doc Ock
doesn't even like her!

YO MAMA is so old,
when she was born the Dead Sea
was just getting sick!

YO MAMA is so weird,
I caught her yelling into the letterbox and
when I asked her what she was doing she said,
"Sending a voice mail."

YO MAMA is so silly, I asked her to
speak her mind and she stayed silent!

YO MAMA is so weird, she entered a
weirdo contest and they said, "Sorry, we
don't allow professionals!"

COMEDY HELPS YOUR MIND STAY SHARP! TRY SOME OF MY **RIDDLES** ON FOR SIZE. ARE YOU SMARTER THAN THESE **DOOFUSES?**

Q: What has a face and two hands but no arms or legs?

A: A clock!

Q: What goes up and doesn't come back down?

A: Your age.

Q: What travels around the world but stays in one spot?

A: A stamp!

Riddles

Q: What can you catch but
not throw?
A: A cold.

 Q: What occurs once in a minute,
twice in a moment and never in
one thousand years?
A: The letter M.

NOW **THAT'S** A STUMPER!

My BRAIN hurts.

 Q: They come out at night without
being called and they are lost in
the day without being stolen.
What are they?
A: Stars!

 Q: Which weighs more, a pound of
feathers or a pound of bricks?
A: Neither, they both weigh one pound!

 Riddles

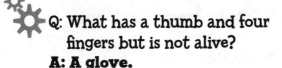

Q: What has a thumb and four fingers but is not alive?
A: A glove.

Q: You walk into a room with a match, a kerosene lamp, a candle and a fireplace. Which do you light first?
A: The match.

That one sounds like a TRICK!

FACEPALM.

Q: What word becomes shorter when you add two letters to it?
A: Short.

Q: If a blue house is made of blue bricks, a yellow house is made of yellow bricks and a red house is made of red bricks, what is a greenhouse made of?
A: Glass.

Riddles

Q: What has a neck but no head?
A: A bottle.

Q: What is at the end of a rainbow?

 A pot of GOLD!

NO, SILLY. **THE LETTER W!** DUH.

Q: Take away my first letter and I still sound the same. Take away my last letter, I still sound the same. Even take away my letter in the middle, I will still sound the same. I'm a five-letter word. What am I?
A: Empty.

Spidey's
OPEN MIC SPOTLIGHT:

> COMING TO THE STAGE RIGHT NOW IS ONE OF THE MOST ANNOYING VILLAINS **OF ALL TIME!** AND HIS COSTUME GIVES ME A HEADACHE. GIVE IT UP FOR **THE SHOCKER!**

 Hey, do you know where the English Channel is? I can't find it on my cable box.

 ...

 So... uh... I'm on that seafood diet...

 IS THAT THE ONE WHERE IF YOU **SEE** FOOD YOU EAT IT?

NO SPOILERS!

 WHEN ARE YOU GOING TO START BEING FUNNY?

The Shocker

Hey, you better pipe down over there! Guess what, web-slinger? YO MAMA loves food SO MUCH that she eats A LOT of it... and... um... sorry. I messed that one up. DARN IT. I'm not so great at this after all.

SHOCKER!

Yes?

NO, I MEANT...
UGH, NEVER MIND.

HERO BUT SOMEHOW
YOU IN THE FACE.

THAT WAS A **ROUGH** DAY.

The GUARDIANS OF THE GALAXY are here to lay down some serious funny business.

HEY, STAR-LORD! UM, IN CASE YOU DIDN'T KNOW, THIS IS **MY** JOKE BOOK. I'LL DO THE INTRODUCTIONS AROUND HERE.

BEAT IT, WEB HEAD! It's our time to shine. Take it away, Gamora...

What do you call a pig that does karate?

A pork chop!

See? Now **THAT'S** comedy.

BUT THIS IS **MY** GIG. I'M THE DUDE WHO MAKES THE FUNNY!

Leave us, slinger of webs. It's **DRAX'S** time to make the funny **NOW.**
Why did the chicken cross the road?
Because he wanted to get to the other side.
HAHAHAHAHAHAHAHAHAHAHAHAHAHAHAHAHA!
Do you get it?

Eh. Okay, so **maybe** we have some work to do.

 I am Groot!

GOOD LUCK, YOU GUYS. (YOU'RE GOING TO NEED IT.)

Q: Why was the salad naked?
A: The waiter forgot to bring the dressing.

Q: What's a boulder's favourite type of music?
A: Rock 'n' roll.

How do you keep a turkey in suspense?

How?

I'll tell you later.

TELL ME NOW!
I DEMAND TO KNOW!

Q: Why was the tree excited
about the future?
A: It was ready to turn over
a new leaf!

Q: Why did the pie go to the dentist?
A: It needed a filling.

Q: What did the earthquake say to
the tornado?
A: It's not my fault!

Q: What's a plumber's favourite vegetable?
A: A leek.

Q: What did the traffic light say to
the car?
A: Don't look now. I'm changing.

Q: Why is a chef the most violent job around?
A: Because they beat eggs and whip cream.

Did you hear that joke about fungus?

No. Why?

It really grows on you.

Q: What did the grape say when DRAX
   stepped on it?
A: It let out a little whine.

Q: What instrument does a cucumber play?
A: A pickle-lo.

Q: Did you hear about the angry pancake?
A: He totally flipped.

WHEN YOU'RE WAY TOO GOOD-LOOKING FOR THIS JOKE BOOK.

Rocket
Where are you? Everyone is on the Milano ready to leave this stinky planet.

I am Groot.

Rocket
In the bathroom?! You shouldn't have eaten so many Xandarian burritos.

I am Groot!

Rocket
It is NOT my fault! I said eat ONE. ONE!!

I am Groot?

Rocket
💀☹😑👍💀☠*!**.....

I am Groot…

Rocket
Oops. That was my butt.

Rocket
I MEAN I SAT ON MY PHONE. IT WAS A BUTT-TEXT! THAT'S WHAT I MEANT.

I am Groot.

Q: Where does a pig store
    its money?
A: A piggy bank.

Q: What do you call a cow
    that's afraid of everything?
A: A cow-ard.

Q: What kind of car does Rocket drive?
A: A Furrari.

 Hahahahahaha!

I don't get it.

Q: Why are cats terrible storytellers?
A: They only have one tail.

Q: What do you get when you cross a pig with a centipede?
A: Bacon and legs.

Q: What kind of cat should you never play games with?
A: A cheetah.

Q: What did the duck say when it bought lipstick?
A: Put it on my bill.

Q: What do you get from a pampered cow?
A: Spoilt milk.

Q: What's the most musical part of a chicken?
A: The drumstick!

Q: Why didn't the butterfly go to the dance?
A: It was a mothball.

Q: Did you hear that Black Panther got 100 per cent on a test?
A: It was a purrfect score.

Q: What lion never roars?
A: A dandeLION!

Q: How does Groot get
   on the internet?
A: He logs on!

Q: What does Groot wear
   to the pool party?
A: Swimming trunks!

Q: What's Groot's
   favourite drink?
A: Root beer!

Q: Why does Groot hate tests?
A: He usually gets stumped!

YO MAMA's glasses are so thick, she can see into the future!

You better watch what you say about my MAMA, fur ball!

OH NO. HERE WE GO.

YO MAMA is so weird, she walked into a haunted house and they offered her a job!

YO MAMA is so lazy, she stuck her nose out the window to let the wind blow it!

YO MAMA's feet are so big, her trainers need number plates.

Yo MAMA is so small, she can use a bottle cap as a surfboard!

 YO MAMA is so silly, she put her air conditioner in backwards so she could chill outside!

YO MAMA is so mean, she threw a boomerang and it never came back!

EVERY DAY I'M

SHUFFLIN'

Spidey's OPEN MIC SPOTLIGHT:

YOU'RE IN FOR A REAL TREAT, LADIES AND GENTLEMAN. UP NEXT WE'VE GOT A GUY WHO IS SUPER FUNNY... **LOOKING.** HA-HA. NO SERIOUSLY, HE'S GREAT – FOR A TALKING ANIMAL! WITHOUT FURTHER ADO: **ROCKET RACCOON!**

Thanks, Spidey. Hey, did you know that YO MAMA is so chatty, I get the busy signal even when I dial the wrong number?

HEH, HEH, HEH. **VERY** FUNNY.

Actually, YO MAMA is so lazy she can't even jump to a conclusion.

OH, IT'S **ON**, YA FILTHY ANIMAL. YO MAMA IS SO SCARY-LOOKING, SHE HAS TO TRICK-OR-TREAT **OVER THE PHONE!** HOW YA LIKE ME NOW?

Rocket Raccoon

What did the tree say to the wind?

HMMM. I need to branch out?

Leaf me alone?

I am GROOOOOT!

One last thing, Spider-Man. How do you plan a space party?

I HAVE **NO** IDEA.

You **PLANET EARLY.**
(MIC DROP)

I WILL NOT MISS YOU GUYS WHEN THIS IS OVER.

NOW IT'S TIME FOR SOME REAL HEROES TO TAKE THE STAGE FOR SOME MIGHTY MARVEL TEAM-UP ACTION. **ROLL CALL!**

I AM DOCTOR STRANGE, MASTER OF THE MYSTIC ARTS AND SORCERER SUPREME.

I AM THE BLACK PANTHER.

KING OF WAKANDA! GOT IT RIGHT THIS TIME. (GO, SPIDEY!)

We're Cloak...

... and Dagger!

I'm Ant-Man.

KING OF ANTS!

No.

PRINCE OF ANTS?

No.

FRIEND TO ANTS?

YOU BET I AM!

Don't forget about me. I'm Miles Morales, the Ultimate Spider-Man.

GOOD TO SEE YOU, KID, BUT NOTHING BEATS THE **ORIGINAL.**

You're AMAZING, but Miles is THE ULTIMATE. He wins.

MIND YOUR ANTS, DUDE!

Q: HOW DOES BLACK PANTHER DO HIS SHOPPING?
A: FROM A **CAT**-A-**LOGUE.**

Q: WHAT'S BLACK PANTHER'S FAVOURITE COLOUR?
A: **PURRR**PLE.

HOW'S IT GOING, BLACK PANTHER?

I'M **FELINE** FINE.

Q: WHAT DO YOU CALL
BLACK PANTHER WHEN
HE'S HAVING A BAD DAY?
A: A SOUR **PUSS.**

Q: What does Ant-Man take when he's ill?
A: **ANTibiotics.**

Q: What do you get when you cross
Ant-Man with some ticks?
A: **ANTics!**

I'm sensing a theme.

YOU'RE BRILLIANT!

Q: What do you call Ant-Man when
he turns one hundred?
A: An **ANTique.**

Q: What does Ant-Man eat for breakfast?
A: **CroissANTs.**

MILES IS A **SMARTY-PANTS** HIGH SCHOOL KID WITH SPIDER POWERS. HMMM. NOW **WHERE** HAVE I SEEN **THAT** BEFORE?

Q: Why did the music teacher need a ladder?
A: To reach the high notes.

Q: What's the worst thing you're likely to find in the school canteen?
A: The food.

Q: What kind of hair do oceans have?
A: Wavy!

Q: What do librarians take with them when they go fishing?
A: Bookworms.

MILES, WHY WAS YOUR HOMEWORK SO SAD?

Because it had too many problems!

Q: Why didn't the sun go to university?
A: Because it already had a million degrees.

Q: What object is king of the classroom?
A: The ruler.

I HAVE A JOKE I WOULD LIKE TO TELL.

 DO YOUR THING, DOC.

 HOW DO YOU MAKE A TISSUE DANCE? YOU PUT A LITTLE BOOGIE IN IT.

IT IS A PLAY ON WORDS.

 IT SURE IS.

 BECAUSE WHEN ONE ENJOYS THE RHYTHMIC MOTION OF DANCING, IT CAN ALSO BE SAID THAT THEY ARE ENJOYING 'THE BOOGIE'.

 I GOT THAT, THANKS.

 I AM A GOOD DANCER, YOU KNOW. DO NOT BE JEALOUS OF MY BOOGIE.

WHY DON'T YOU JUST STICK TO MAGIC, DOC? (THIS GUY IS **SOOO** WEIRD.)

WHEN YOUR FRIENDS DON'T BELIEVE YOU HANG OUT WITH A RICH PRINCE SO YOU GOTTA SNAP A SELFIE FOR PROOF.

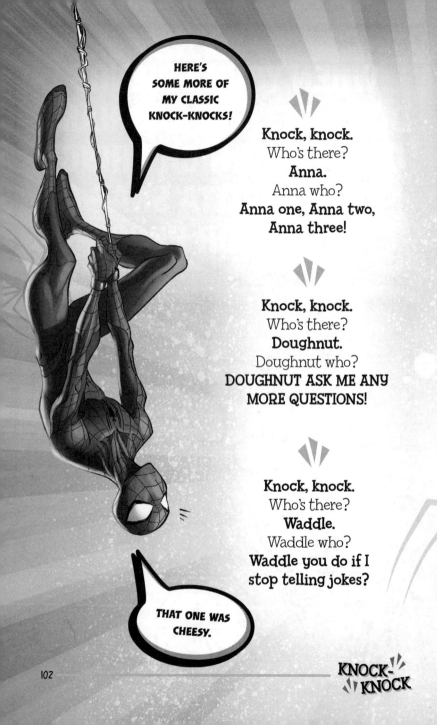

HERE'S SOME MORE OF MY CLASSIC KNOCK-KNOCKS!

Knock, knock.
Who's there?
Anna.
Anna who?
Anna one, Anna two, Anna three!

Knock, knock.
Who's there?
Doughnut.
Doughnut who?
DOUGHNUT ASK ME ANY MORE QUESTIONS!

Knock, knock.
Who's there?
Waddle.
Waddle who?
Waddle you do if I stop telling jokes?

THAT ONE WAS CHEESY.

KNOCK-KNOCK

Knock, knock.
Who's there?
Queso.
Queso who?
Queso mistaken identity.

Knock, knock.
Who's there?
I am.
I am who?
You mean you don't know?

Knock, knock.
Who's there?
Yoda.
Yoda who?
**Yoda weirdest person
I've ever met.**

That one was **SUPER** cheesy.

Knock, knock.
Who's there?
Ken.
Ken who?
Ken you hear me now?

Knock, knock.
Who's there?
Alison.
Alison who?
Alison to you, but you have to listen to me first!

Knock, knock.

Ben.

Ben away for a while, but now I'm back! Miss me?

WHO'S THERE?

BEN WHO?

EH.

KNOCK-KNOCK

Me: My Super Hero suit is going to be cool. Not too cheesy or tigh—

Me to me: Tight. Make it skintight. Add spiderwebs.

OH MAN. I DON'T KNOW IF I CAN TAKE ANY MORE **YO MAMA JOKES.**

Is it because **YO MAMA** is so silly she went to the beach to **surf** the **Internet?**

NO, IT'S BECAUSE YO MAMA IS SO BORING, I CAN'T THINK OF ANY MORE JOKES!

YO MAMA is so small, she can do **limbo under the door!**

YO MAMA IS SO... NORMAL, SHE JUST SITS AT HOME AND LIVES HER LIFE!

Yo Mama Jokes

YO MAMA is so hungry, when she hears it's **chilly** outside she grabs a **spoon** and some **crackers!**

 YO MAMA IS SO BUFF, SHE CAN DO THE **BACKSTROKE IN MUD!**

 That last one was kind of a **compliment.**

I CAN DO THIS **ALL DAY!**

Yo Mama Jokes

YO MAMA IS SO TINY THAT HER BEST FRIEND IS AN **ANT!**

MY best friend is an ant.

THIS GUY AND ANTS! GIVE IT A REST, WILL YOU? ANTS ARE COOL. **WE GET IT.**

Do you? Do you get it? Because I heard YO MAMA is so big, when she turns round, her friends throw her a **'welcome back'** party!

WOULDJA LOOK AT THAT. ANT-MAN IS **FINALLY** GETTING THE HANG OF THIS.

Yo Mama Jokes

AND NOW...
CLOAK AND DAGGER
TELL A YO MAMA JOKE!

YO MAMA is so lazy...

... she has a stay-at-home job and still can't get to work on time!

THIS HAS BEEN...
CLOAK AND DAGGER
TELL A
**YO MAMA
JOKE!**

Spider-Man

Hey, Groot! Are you coming to the party? It's insane! Everyone is asking about you. Doc Strange is wearing a lamp shade on his head already. It's hilarious.

I am Groot.

Spider-Man

You knew it was at 4:00 p.m. That's what the invite said! We need you here NOW, dude. You were in charge of bringing the crisps and salsa!

I am Groot!

Spider-Man

I wasn't yelling. I was just being firm. I'm also dying of starvation. Listen, you're our buddy and we all want you to come hang out.

I am Groot?

Spider-Man

Yes!

I am Groot!!!

Spider-Man

AWESOME. See you soon! And don't forget about those crisps and salsa.

AND NOW THE MOMENT YOU'VE BEEN WAITING FOR... THE JOKE WALL AT **THE END OF THE UNIVERSE!**

I wasn't waiting for this moment. I'm kind of bored and need a nap! What about you, Black Panther?

I FEEL THAT I HAVE DONE WHAT I CAME HERE TO DO AND AM FULFILLED.

YOU GUYS! I'M TRYING TO RUN A **JOKE BOOK** HERE AND WE'RE ALMOST AT THE FINISH LINE. ARE YOU SURE YOU DON'T HAVE **ONE** MORE AWESOME JOKE IN YOU? PRETTY PLEASE?

Sorry, Spidey. I've got homework.

OOOF. THOSE GUYS ARE **EXHAUSTING.** LET'S SINK OUR TEETH INTO SOME TANTALIZING TONGUE TWISTERS THAT'LL KEEP YOU ON YOUR TOES.

SIX SICKLY SPIDERS SPUN SPECIAL SNARES.
SIX SICKLY SPIDERS SPUN SPECIAL SNARES.
SIX SICKLY SPIDERS SPUN SPECIAL SNARES.

THE BUGS BUZZED AND BUGGED BUZZ.
THE BUGS BUZZED AND BUGGED BUZZ.
THE BUGS BUZZED AND BUGGED BUZZ.

TONGUE TWISTERS

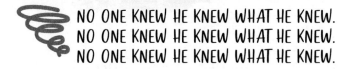
NO ONE KNEW HE KNEW WHAT HE KNEW.
NO ONE KNEW HE KNEW WHAT HE KNEW.
NO ONE KNEW HE KNEW WHAT HE KNEW.

TOY BOAT.
TOY BOAT.
TOY BOAT.

WET WINTER WEATHER WITH WICKED WET WINDS.
WET WINTER WEATHER WITH WICKED WET WINDS.
WET WINTER WEATHER WITH WICKED WET WINDS.

HEARTY HEROES HIT HEAVY HENCHMEN.
HEARTY HEROES HIT HEAVY HENCHMEN.
HEARTY HEROES HIT HEAVY HENCHMEN.

J. JONAH JAMESON JUMPED JAUNTILY.
J. JONAH JAMESON JUMPED JAUNTILY.
J. JONAH JAMESON JUMPED JAUNTILY.

STEVE SAVED SAILING SEALS SITTING SIDE BY SIDE.
STEVE SAVED SAILING SEALS SITTING SIDE BY SIDE.
STEVE SAVED SAILING SEALS SITTING SIDE BY SIDE.

PEPPER POTTS PLACED PICKLED PEARS
    ON THE PRETTY PERCH.
PEPPER POTTS PLACED PICKLED PEARS
    ON THE PRETTY PERCH.
PEPPER POTTS PLACED PICKLED PEARS
    ON THE PRETTY PERCH.

CHOP SHOPS STOCK CHOPS.
CHOP SHOPS STOCK CHOPS.
CHOP SHOPS STOCK CHOPS.

TONGUE TWISTERS

UNIQUE NEW YORK!
UNIQUE NEW YORK!
UNIQUE NEW YORK!

GREG GUARDED GREEN GOBLIN'S GLIDER.
GREG GUARDED GREEN GOBLIN'S GLIDER.
GREG GUARDED GREEN GOBLIN'S GLIDER.

TAMMY TRAINS TARANTULAS IN A
TERRIBLE TENNESSEE TOWN. TRAIN, TAMMY, TRAIN!
TAMMY TRAINS TARANTULAS IN A
TERRIBLE TENNESSEE TOWN. TRAIN, TAMMY, TRAIN!
TAMMY TRAINS TARANTULAS IN A
TERRIBLE TENNESSEE TOWN. TRAIN, TAMMY, TRAIN!

TAMMY, YOU HAVE THE **WEIRDEST** JOB OF ALL TIME.

STUPID SUPERSTITION!
STUPID SUPERSTITION!
STUPID SUPERSTITION!

 TONGUE TWISTERS

WISE WITCHES WISH WEIRD WISHES.
WHICH WEIRD WISHES DID WISE WITCHES WISH?
WISE WITCHES WISH WEIRD WISHES.
WHICH WEIRD WISHES DID WISE WITCHES WISH?
WISE WITCHES WISH WEIRD WISHES.
WHICH WEIRD WISHES DID WISE WITCHES WISH?

 VULTURE VOWED: "A VALIANT VACATION!"
VULTURE VOWED: "A VALIANT VACATION!"
VULTURE VOWED: "A VALIANT VACATION!"

I SCREAM!
YOU SCREAM!
WE ALL **SCREAM**
FOR ICE CREAM!

TONGUE
TWISTERS

Spider-Man @WallCrawlerNYC
So bored sitting on the top of this bank. DRAMATIC SIGH. I hope a scientist with octopus tentacles doesn't try to steal all the $$$ inside.

Spider-Man @WallCrawlerNYC
Now it's raining! Webbed up a little umbrella. Feelin' cosy. Oh no. I feel pigeons on top of it. Or as I like to call them, DEMON SKY RATS!

Spider-Man @WallCrawlerNYC
GAH! The pigeons are ATTACKING me! I REPEAT, THE PIGEONS ARE ATTACKING ME! Someone call for help! Uh-oh. Bank alarm going off. BRB

Spider-Man @WallCrawlerNYC
Robbery = foiled by ME. YOU'RE WELCOME, NYC. Dumb ol' Doc Ock read my tweet and fell for my trap. What a bonehead. Gonna go nap. Laterz!

WHO DOESN'T LOVE RIDDLES?
THESE ARE SOME REAL STUMPERS.
SEE IF YOU CAN FIGURE THEM OUT.
WHEN YOU'RE READY TO CHECK
YOUR WORK, THERE'S AN ANSWER KEY
ON PAGE 123.
DON'T CHEAT!

1. You can make it, but you can't see it. What is it?

2. Poor people have it. Rich people need it. If you eat it, you die. What is it?

3. What is always in front of you but you can't see it?

4. It is as light as a feather, but most people are unable to hold it for more than a minute. What is it?

Riddles

5. What needs to be broken before you can use it?

6. Scott's father had three sons: Alex, Gabriel and...?

7. What word is spelt incorrectly in every dictionary?

8. What has one eye but can't see?

9. If I have it, I don't share it. If I share it, I don't have it. What is it?

10. What can you hold but never touch?

11. How much dirt is in a hole that's twelve feet deep and five feet wide?

12. There was a ship filled with people, but there wasn't a single person on the ship. Why?

Riddles

ANSWER KEY

1. Noise.

2. Nothing.

3. The future.

4. Their breath.

5. An egg.

6. Scott.

7. Incorrectly.

8. A needle.

9. A secret.

10. A conversation.

11. None. It's a hole.

12. They were all married.

SOOOO, HOW'D YOU DO?

Spidey's OPEN MIC SPOTLIGHT:

 AND NOW THE MOMENT YOU'VE ALL BEEN WAITING FOR: **THE MAIN EVENT!** OUR FINAL COMEDIAN IS A MASTER JOKESTER. HE'S THE KING OF...

Get on with it! Less **TALK**, more **JOKES**.

 Yeah! Let's see what you got, Spidey!

ALL RIGHT! ALL RIGHT! COMING TO THE STAGE RIGHT NOW, **IT'S ME, THE AMAZING SPIDER-MAN!**

The Amazing Spider-Man!

KNOCK, KNOCK.
WHO'S THERE?
COWS GO.
COWS GO WHO?
NO SILLY, COWS
GO MOO!

Booooooo! Cow humour! Even worse than spider humour.

OH, YEAH? WELL, WHAT DO YOU CALL A BAD COMEDIAN?

Rocket Racoon.

HA! HIGH FIVE, ANT-KID!

... I'm just gonna let that one go.

WHY DID DRAX THROW A SIDE OF BEEF ON AN ASTEROID? HE WANTED TO MAKE A MEATY-OR!

LIES! ALL LIES!

CAPTAIN AMERICA IS SO OLD.

How old is he?

CAPTAIN AMERICA IS SO OLD, WHEN HE WAS BORN RAINBOWS WERE BLACK AND WHITE!

HA! THAT'S FUNNY. YOU'RE GOOD AT THIS COMEDY THING.

I'M SPIDER-MAN. I DO WHATEVER A SPIDER CAN. THANK YOU AND GOODNIGHT!

CONGRATULATIONS!
...OU MADE IT. YOU ARE AN OFFICIAL MASTER OF COMEDY. HOW DOES IT FEEL? I BET IT FEELS TINGLY. I HOPE YOU WEREN'T EXPECTING AN HONOURARY CERTIFICATE. I'M ALL OUT.

SO NOW THAT YOU KNOW ALL THERE IS TO KNOW ABOUT JOKES, WHY NOT WRITE A FEW NEW ONES? DON'T BE SHY. **GET CREATIVE.**

HOW ABOUT A **KNOCK-KNOCK?** GIVE IT A WHIRL.

THINK UP A GOOD **SET-UP** AND **PUNCH LINE.** I KNOW YOU'VE GOT ONE IN YOU.

GO WILD! LET YOUR CREATIVE SPIRIT RUN FREE!

OKAY, MAYBE NOT **THAT FREE.**